It's another Quality Book from CGP

This book has been carefully written
for Key Stage Two children learning punctuation.

It's full of tricky exercises designed to give
them lots of punctuation practice.

Each exercise has a space for you to set a target score,
so that each child knows exactly what they're aiming for.

What CGP is all about

Our sole aim here at CGP is to produce the highest quality books
— carefully written, immaculately presented and
dangerously close to being funny.

Then we work our socks off to get them out to you
— at the cheapest possible prices.

Capital letters and full stops

Re-write these sentences, putting in the missing capital letters and full stops.
[ ] out of 20 or more will get you into Punctuation Paradise.

1) norman and nigel are always being naughty

2) joey's my favourite but i don't like ross

3) i thought it would be sunny in france

4) sadly, when i went on holiday there it rained

5) next time i won't go in november

6) i crashed my remote controlled car

7) my sister louise wasn't pleased

8) it wasn't my fault her legs were in the way

9) joe lives in manchester now but he's moving

10) soon he'll live in london, but i can still visit

11) i'm a fast runner, but chloe's the fastest

12) "quiet, class!" yelled mrs shoutalot

13) i wouldn't mind, but she's not even a teacher

14) she was just walking past the open window

15) my neighbour tony has a pet called rover

16) he's getting a bit too big for his hutch

17) not surprising really, as rover's an elephant

18) sam wants to play football for liverpool

19) i'd rather go to hollywood and be an actor

20) my sister abigail says she's going to be a vet

Extra sentences

E1) mr crustington is a baker in birmingham

E2) i told kevin i lived in a lighthouse

1) ....

2) ....

3) ....

4) ....

5) ....

6) ....

7) ....

8) ....

9) ....

10) ....

11) ....

12) ....

13) ....

14) ....

15) ....

16) ....

17) ....

18) ....

19) ....

20) ....

Extra sentences

E1) ....

E2) ....

Capital letters and full stops

Re-write these sentences, putting in the missing capital letters and full stops.
[ ] out of 20 or more will get you into Punctuation Paradise.

1) paul thinks he's perfect, he's really vain

2) i really wish my dad would stop singing

3) he pretends he's elvis — how embarrassing

4) at least he doesn't pretend he's britney spears

5) i'm spinning around, move out of my way

6) the sheep in my garden keep eating the roses

7) derek is daft about dolphins — he loves them

8) he even went swimming with some in florida

9) now liz wants to go and see lions in africa

10) she'd better not though, she'll end up a snack

11) the spider in my bath was doing backstroke

12) the earwig in the shed was doing aerobics

13) insects are doing more exercise these days

14) brainy belinda got a calculator on her birthday

15) i'm so glad i got a skateboard instead

16) my dog maisie is getting really fat

17) i've told my brother dave not to feed her crisps

18) fergus flew through the open window

19) then he limped back into the house

20) my name is adam, and i'm an acrobat

Extra sentences

E1) my friend antonio is from italy and he's visiting england soon

E2) if sophie eats one more cake, she'll explode

Capital letters and full stops

1) ....

2) ....

3) ....

4) ....

5) ....

6) ....

7) ....

8) ....

9) ....

10) ....

11) ....

12) ....

13) ....

14) ....

15) ....

16) ....

17) ....

18) ....

19) ....

20) ....

Extra sentences

E1) ....

E2) ....

Capital letters and full stops

Re-write these sentences, putting in the missing capital letters and full stops.
☐ out of 20 or more will get you into Punctuation Paradise.

1) gina's grandma lives in india

2) philip's grandad lives in scotland

3) my grandparents live on my street

4) the cat next door loves pickled herring

5) she's called smokey, because she's grey

6) claire has a cat too — his name is snowy

7) you can probably guess his colour

8) london is the capital city of england

9) paris is the capital city of france

10) that's as far as we got in class today — i think

11) i know belinda got the best mark in the test

12) still, i think it might be me next time

13) mrs knowslots, our teacher, says i'm doing well

14) when we go camping we cook beans in a pan

15) manchester united is my favourite team

16) my brother dave supports west ham

17) my sister louise doesn't like football

18) she prefers rugby, and likes ice hockey too

19) helen can touch her nose with her tongue

20) i know a dog called maisie who can do that too

Extra sentences

E1) "your modern music is all rubbish," said old mrs mooper

E2) after two hours, michael was sick of watching adverts

Capital letters and full stops

1) ....

2) ....

3) ....

4) ....

5) ....

6) ....

7) ....

8) ....

9) ....

10) ....

11) ....

12) ....

13) ....

14) ....

15) ....

16) ....

17) ....

18) ....

19) ....

20) ....

Extra sentences

E1) ....

E2) ....

Capital letters and full stops

Re-write these sentences, putting in the missing capital letters and full stops.
☐ out of 20 or more will get you into Punctuation Paradise.

1) mary-kate and ashley annoy my brother dave

2) most of the time, my brother dave annoys me

3) i really like my aunt jane's new baby

4) she's going to call it either mary or sarah

5) sarah's nice, but i'd rather call her grizelda

6) "i'm singing in the rain," sang matilda

7) she wasn't though, she was just in the shower

8) a dog called brian chased leaves in the park

9) a cat called ken chased his tail

10) mr trotter's ducks are on their way to devon

11) the name of the station was chuggington

12) benny is a baboon from brazil

13) if the goats are rude, send them home

14) my new dentist comes from memphis

15) his uncle stan comes from milan

16) the dragon's lunchbox melted in the heat

17) the cat next door has buried maisie

18) david beckham has a son called brooklyn

19) brooklyn is named after a place in new york

20) i get my hair cut at a salon called snippers

Extra sentences

E1) if you eat any more peas, liz, you'll turn into one

E2) if you throw any more peas at liz, colin, you're in trouble

Capital letters and full stops

1) ....

2) ....

3) ....

4) ....

5) ....

6) ....

7) ....

8) ....

9) ....

10) ....

11) ....

12) ....

13) ....

14) ....

15) ....

16) ....

17) ....

18) ....

19) ....

20) ....

Extra sentences

E1) ....

E2) ....

Capital letters and full stops

Some of the girls in class 4B have decided to form a new girl band. it was elizabeth's idea, so she's the lead singer. the other girls in the band are Amy, Zoe and jessica

their school is called allerton Primary School, so they've named the band The Allerton allstars Zoe reckons they're going to be the new Girls aloud — Elizabeth says she hopes they'll be a bit better than that!

The Allerton Allstars have already written a song It's called I Love Chocolate. Their teacher, Mr mudswipe, thinks it sounds like The spice Girls in their early days. tommy Meanthorpe from Year Five says it sounds more like a cat having its tail trodden on

The girls are hoping The Allerton allstars will be discovered by simon Cowell in time for i love Chocolate to be the christmas number one.

Capital letters and full stops

....

....

....

....

....

....

....

....

....

....

....

....

....

....

....

....

....

....

....

....

....

....

....

Commas

Re-write these sentences, putting in the missing commas.
[ ] out of 20 or more will get you into Punctuation Paradise.

1) Today I bought wine gums toffees and fudge.

2) Tom's sisters are called Helen Steph and Kate.

3) British flags are red white and blue.

4) Mel loves maths science and P.E. — she's mad!

5) Alan's been to Egypt France Spain and Wales.

6) My rabbits like carrots apples lettuce and pears.

7) They don't like cakes chocolate or crisps.

8) Little Liz plays with footballs Lego and computers.

9) Her big brother prefers teddies dolls and tea-sets.

10) Sam's lived in Liverpool Manchester and Leeds.

11) Tennis rugby and cricket are my favourite sports.

12) Mrs Stomper teaches us maths english and art.

13) I bought new shoes trousers a jacket and a bag.

14) We saw lions tigers bears and bison at the zoo.

15) At the party there was ice cream cake and jelly.

16) I play sport on Mondays Fridays and Sundays.

17) Brian collects pens pies and toenail clippings.

18) They had pigs cows and hens on the farm.

19) I love Cameron Diaz Brad Pitt and Lucy Liu.

20) My dad can play the flute piano and guitar.

Extra sentences

E1) My hobbies include singing dancing and falling over.

E2) On his birthday Liam got a bike a T.V. and a surprise party.

Commas

1) ....

2) ....

3) ....

4) ....

5) ....

6) ....

7) ....

8) ....

9) ....

10) ....

11) ....

12) ....

13) ....

14) ....

15) ....

16) ....

17) ....

18) ....

19) ....

20) ....

Extra sentences

E1) ....

E2) ....

Commas

1) Jim fell out of bed and hurt his leg arm and toe.

2) In Scotland they have haggis kilts and lochs.

3) It rained then hailed then snowed!

4) I can count to ten in French Italian and Welsh.

5) "Staying alive staying alive" sang Roy badly.

6) The bad dog chases ducks birds and cats.

7) His shaggy coat is black brown and white.

8) In summer Lyn sunbathes all day.

9) Claire's scared of spiders she hates their legs.

10) At playtime we skipped shouted and ran races.

11) Adam came first Hannah second and Phil third.

12) My friends are all on holiday I wish I was too.

13) Dave is very tall he just keeps on growing.

14) Our cat loves milk she'd drink a pint a day.

15) At the circus we saw clowns jugglers and lions.

16) Faye's hair is blonde long and curly.

17) So was her sister's until she dyed it blue!

18) In our school play I was the farmer's son.

19) My friend was a tree he didn't get to move!

20) His costume made him hot he was really cross.

Extra sentences

E1) "Moan moan moan that's all young folk do" said the old man.

E2) Owls foxes and badgers are nocturnal they sleep all day.

Commas

1) ....

2) ....

3) ....

4) ....

5) ....

6) ....

7) ....

8) ....

9) ....

10) ....

11) ....

12) ....

13) ....

14) ....

15) ....

16) ....

17) ....

18) ....

19) ....

20) ....

Extra sentences

E1) ....

E2) ....

Commas

1) Jason Jack and Harry are the terrible twins.

2) I watch Friends Hollyoaks and The Simpsons.

3) Sadly mum's trifle melted all over her feet.

4) Fred the dragon eats coal petrol and matches.

5) My horse Bob canters trots and gallops.

6) Jill loves Justin Timberlake she's got every CD.

7) "Hurry up" said mum "or we won't go at all."

8) My sister wears lots of ribbons lace and pink.

9) Even in winter she walks around in a tutu.

10) Helen does tap ballet and modern dance.

11) Her costumes shoes and tights fill a wardrobe.

12) In the summer I'll get six weeks holiday.

13) I'm nearly nine I'll be in double figures soon!

14) To me that's old but my gran's almost eighty.

15) I passed the ball to Ken which was a bad idea.

16) He kicked it his hardest straight at a window.

17) Worst of all the window was our headmaster's!

18) We all got in trouble especially Ken.

19) If I was famous I'd be in all my favourite shows.

20) For tea I'm going to have curry rice and chips.

Extra sentences

E1) The fat hairy dog growled showing big yellow teeth.

E2) "Quick let's get out of here" yelled Tony trembling.

Commas

1) ....

2) ....

3) ....

4) ....

5) ....

6) ....

7) ....

8) ....

9) ....

10) ....

11) ....

12) ....

13) ....

14) ....

15) ....

16) ....

17) ....

18) ....

19) ....

20) ....

Extra sentences

E1) ....

E2) ....

Commas

Pegasus Circus came to our town not long ago. I went to see the show with my three brothers whose names are Jim Tim and freddy.

On the posters we'd seen pictures of lions tigers bears and elephants. We were really excited It started well, with some very funny clowns. There were acrobats jugglers and magicians too but no animals.

we'd only come to see the animals really so we were getting cross. It didn't help when some performing hens came out, followed by sheep then goats then cows.

"This is rubbish," said Freddy, "i can see all these kinds of animals any time on the farm next door."

I told him we should wait for the last bit and see if it was any better but he wouldn't stop grumbling It turned out to be worth waiting for though when they led a horse with wings into the ring.

"That's rubbish too those wings are stuck on," Freddy whined. then the horse flew over to Freddy stuck its tongue out at him then zoomed off again.

Commas

Question marks & exclamation marks

Re-write these sentences, putting in the missing question marks and exclamation marks.
☐ out of 20 or more will get you into Punctuation Paradise.

1) "Help Help" shouted the sinking teacher.

2) What time is it I'm going to be late

3) Is that a huge spider on your head

4) Why did it have to rain on sports day again

5) Every single year, it's always the same

6) Why are the audience clapping

7) That was the worst play I've ever seen

8) Even the actors fell asleep, it was so dull

9) "How many beans make five" asked Tim.

10) "What a peculiar question" said the teacher.

11) That was the loudest burp I've ever heard

12) Where have my goats wandered off to now

13) Oh no My mum's about to do karaoke

14) Run Run The lion's catching up

15) How can you deny it It's so obvious

16) You are the one who ate all my lemons

17) How else can you explain your yellow mouth

18) "Why are we waiting" sang the naughty girls.

19) Put down that penguin at once

20) When are we going home

Extra sentences

E1) Romeo Romeo Where on earth have you got to now, Romeo

E2) "Please can I go to school on Saturday" begged odd Ozzy.

1) ....

2) ....

3) ....

4) ....

5) ....

6) ....

7) ....

8) ....

9) ....

10) ....

11) ....

12) ....

13) ....

14) ....

15) ....

16) ....

17) ....

18) ....

19) ....

20) ....

Extra sentences

E1) ....

E2) ....

Question marks & exclamation marks

Re-write these sentences, putting in the missing question marks and exclamation marks.
☐ out of 20 or more will get you into Punctuation Paradise.

1) "Boo Rubbish" shouted my grandad.

2) It was a bit mean — at my sister's school play

3) Where's Belgium Is it somewhere near France

4) I dreamed about a carrot that sprouted wings

5) Then it flew up my nose What a nightmare

6) Why can't my cat and my dog just get along

7) Can you please cook my tea and make my bed

8) No Certainly not You must do it yourself.

9) Which witches live in those two cottages

10 Why was Matthew off school last week

11) He had chicken pox, he was covered in spots

12) "Who do you think you are" yelled Barney.

13) "I have absolutely no idea" exclaimed the snail.

14) Who's stolen my cherry pie Come on, own up

15) Bang Boom Whoosh I just love fireworks

16) Why can't my family just be normal for once

17) My mum won't stop juggling for five minutes

18) Dad's keeping donkeys in the dining room

19) And where's my brother Living in the shed

20) Still, I can't talk — I've got treacle on my head

Extra sentences

E1) "Can I have some more Well, I don't see why not" said Oliver.

E2) Why do some trees lose their leaves in autumn Poor things

Question marks & exclamation marks

1) ....

2) ....

3) ....

4) ....

5) ....

6) ....

7) ....

8) ....

9) ....

10) ....

11) ....

12) ....

13) ....

14) ....

15) ....

16) ....

17) ....

18) ....

19) ....

20) ....

Extra sentences

E1) ....

E2) ....

Question marks & exclamation marks

Re-write these sentences, putting in the missing question marks and exclamation marks.
___ out of 20 or more will get you into Punctuation Paradise.

1) For goodness sake, have a bath

2) "Can't you take a joke" asked the comedian.

3) Why does it rain so much where I live

4) Did you know horses can sleep standing up

5) Elephants are big, but whales are massive

6) My brother is so annoying, it's unbelievable

7) When is your birthday I can't wait for mine

8) If my wig blows away, will you help me catch it

9) "Come on the reds" shouted the football fan.

10) Alex was so excited, he spilled his apple juice

11) The dog barked loudly and the postman ran off

12) "Hey What about my letters" called its owner.

13) What's brown and sticky   *A stick*

14) Why do I have to wear a coat It's not even cold

15) "Why's our puppy getting so big" said its owner.

16) "Because he's really a bear cub" said the vet.

17) "Goodness" said the owner, "What will I do"

18) "Why not put him in a zoo" the vet suggested.

19) My dad has the loudest sneeze in the world

20) Where, oh where, can my brother be hiding

Extra sentences

E1) "Why aren't you in bed It's past ten" my mum exclaimed.

E2) "I'm too excited Why aren't you" answered my cheeky sister.

Question marks & exclamation marks

1) ....

2) ....

3) ....

4) ....

5) ....

6) ....

7) ....

8) ....

9) ....

10) ....

11) ....

12) ....

13) ....

14) ....

15) ....

16) ....

17) ....

18) ....

19) ....

20) ....

Extra sentences

E1) ....

E2) ....

Question marks & exclamation marks

Jemma and Jake were walking home from school. Suddenly, they heard a terrible screeching from a house at the top of their road.

"Help me Help me" somebody was wailing, "Please, won't someone help me"

"Isn't that Mrs cherry's voice" Jake asked his sister.

"It sounds like her. We've got to do something" jemma replied.

They rushed into the house. There they saw Mrs Cherry clutching her young son Arthur — who was bright green

"my baby needs help" yelled Mrs Cherry when she saw them, "He's turned green"

"He's got red splodges too" gasped Jemma, examining the baby. "Is he ill"

"I think I know the answer" Jake exclaimed. "Has arthur been playing with paint"

He pointed to something in the corner, which looked a lot like an empty paint tin.

"You bad boy Arthur" Mrs Cherry scolded, "You were supposed to be painting a picture, not yourself"

"i think all he needs is a bath, don't you" laughed Jemma.

Apostrophes

Re-write these sentences, putting in the missing apostrophes.
☐ out of 20 or more will get you into Punctuation Paradise.

1) The boys homework was eaten by his dog.

2) The gardeners arms were sore from digging.

3) Marys baby brother is a real pest.

4) He got chocolate on Marys new dress.

5) Are those Bens football boots?

6) The old mans flowery hat looked rather odd.

7) It was his wifes, which he'd put on by mistake.

8) "Jill, take your foot out of Jims face," said mum.

9) The grey ponys name was Polly.

10) Dans trainers are smelly, but Toms are worse.

11) Carolines computer is great — it's brand new.

12) The old mans wife wants her hat back.

13) But it keeps the old mans ears nice and warm.

14) My friend Emmas house is up for sale.

15) It's her dads idea — he wants a bigger house.

16) This tent is Adams, and that one is Pauls.

17) My little sisters doll is called Loopy Lucy.

18) Barbaras singing is nearly as loud as Jens.

19) It is my uncles ambition to do a bungee jump.

20) It is my aunts ambition to stop him!

Extra sentences

E1) Helens mums favourite food is cheese on toast.

E2) It was my grandads friend Marvins birthday last week.

1) ....

2) ....

3) ....

4) ....

5) ....

6) ....

7) ....

8) ....

9) ....

10) ....

11) ....

12) ....

13) ....

14) ....

15) ....

16) ....

17) ....

18) ....

19) ....

20) ....

Extra sentences

E1) ....

E2) ....

Apostrophes

Re-write these sentences, putting in the missing apostrophes.
☐ out of 20 or more will get you into Punctuation Paradise.

1)   The dentists chair is quite a scary place.

2)   The womens football team beat the mens.

3)   I caught a cold at the doctors surgery.

4)   Both the burglars faces were hidden.

5)   All the firefighters drinks went cold.

6)   The choirs songs were lovely to hear.

7)   Every one of the singers voices was in tune.

8)   Jennys sisters dog looks like a wolf.

9)   The childrens teacher hid in the cupboard.

10) All the bridesmaids dresses were green.

11) Jessies cat Feathers has had six kittens.

12) All the kittens coats are black and white.

13) I hate rats tails — they're all long and wriggly.

14) But I don't mind rats faces — they're quite nice.

15) The ponies tails and manes were tangled.

16) Those four footballers skills are fantastic.

17) Wish they'd come and play for my schools side!

18) Dad said he was going to the mens room.

19) But he accidentally went into the ladies instead!

20) You should have seen the poor mans face.

Extra sentences

E1) My cars engine is so small, dogs overtake me.

E2) All the other cars top speeds are twice as fast.

Apostrophes

1) ....

2) ....

3) ....

4) ....

5) ....

6) ....

7) ....

8) ....

9) ....

10) ....

11) ....

12) ....

13) ....

14) ....

15) ....

16) ....

17) ....

18) ....

19) ....

20) ....

Extra sentences

E1) ....

E2) ....

Apostrophes

Re-write these sentences, putting in the missing apostrophes.
□ out of 20 or more will get you into Punctuation Paradise.

1) My sister says she didnt break mums vase.

2) My brother says he didnt do it either.

3) Im sure it wasnt me — must have been the cat.

4) "That fat cat couldnt jump up there," said mum.

5) Everyone watched as dads face turned red.

6) "I didnt mean to do it," he muttered sheepishly.

7) I dont know if I believe him — he never liked it.

8) Kevin doesnt care where he goes on holiday.

9) As long as its hot, Kevins quite happy.

10) The baby next door cant count up to ten.

11) Shes almost there, but she misses out eight.

12) "It isnt my fault!" wailed our teacher.

13) "I try to teach them but they just wont listen!"

14) Now shes hiding under her desk.

15) We shouldve listened, and Im sorry we didnt.

16) You cant catch a cat if he doesnt want you to.

17) Thats something Ive learned today.

18) Ive got the scratches to prove it too.

19) Mark isnt a bad player and Jasons quite good.

20) But I wouldnt say theyre both better than me.

Extra sentences

E1) Youve said youre sorry and Ive forgiven you.

E2) Julie wouldnt take Jessies coat — Im sure she wouldnt dare!

Apostrophes

1) ....

2) ....

3) ....

4) ....

5) ....

6) ....

7) ....

8) ....

9) ....

10) ....

11) ....

12) ....

13) ....

14) ....

15) ....

16) ....

17) ....

18) ....

19) ....

20) ....

Extra sentences

E1) ....

E2) ....

Apostrophes

Meg's birthday had only just begun, and already itd been a total disaster. First, her mum had burned her special birthday breakfast.

"Im sorry Meg," her mum said, "Its my fault, and Im afraid Ive no time to cook another. Ive got to go out and collect something."

So Meg had to have boring old cereal. While she was eating it, her little brothers breakfast somehow got all over her new clothes.

"Dad!" wailed Meg, "Barneys boiled eggs all over me! And the postmans late so I havent got any cards! Its my birthday and everythings ruined!"

"Dont worry Meg," her dad said, "Your mums back. Maybe shes brought a present to cheer you up."

Meg didnt think anything could cheer her up by that time. But then she saw what her mum had in her arms. It was two puppies — just what shed always wanted.

The puppies tails were wagging. Mum put them down and they waddled over to see Meg.

"I cant believe it!" Meg cried, as they licked boiled egg off her new trousers. "This is the best birthday ever!"

Apostrophes

Speech marks

Re-write these sentences, putting in the missing speech marks.
☐ out of 20 or more will get you into Punctuation Paradise.

1) Don't enter, beware, whispered the old man.

2) But it's just the gate to our garden, said Jack.

3) Oh right, go ahead then, the old man replied.

4) Jack asked, Where's your medicine, grandad?

5) Yes, I should go and get it, agreed his grandad.

6) Where are you going? shouted mum.

7) Out! my bad brother called back, racing past.

8) Oops, said Bob, as he plunged down the well.

9) Don't worry son, called the rescue team.

10) We'll get you out! they promised, loudly.

11) Thanks, replied Bob, I'm a bit cold and wet.

12) The man said, Darling, let us run away together.

13) Get lost, your breath smells, said his girlfriend.

14) We are the cheeky girls, sang my gran.

15) Wild horses couldn't drag me away, said Bill.

16) You're coming with us, said the wild horses.

17) Your house is huge! gasped Molly.

18) Actually, this is just my room, said Jim smugly.

19) Can I have more milk? the cat seemed to say.

20) Shaun wondered, why do monkeys live in trees?

Extra sentences

E1) Run! shouted dad, The buffalo are coming! Save yourselves!

E2) Be quiet, snapped mum, It's the middle of the night.

Speech marks

1) ....

2) ....

3) ....

4) ....

5) ....

6) ....

7) ....

8) ....

9) ....

10) ....

11) ....

12) ....

13) ....

14) ....

15) ....

16) ....

17) ....

18) ....

19) ....

20) ....

Extra sentences

E1) ....

E2) ....

Speech marks

Re-write these sentences, putting in the missing speech marks.

[ ] out of 20 or more will get you into Punctuation Paradise.

1) Stop, thief! shouted the shopkeeper, Stop!

2) I've already paid, said Santa crossly.

3) Pardon me, chuckled dad after his loud burp.

4) Get up or you'll be late, nagged my mum.

5) I've hurt my knee, the ice-skater told the doctor.

6) I'll be back, insisted Arnie.

7) Will whined, Mum, this cake tastes of sawdust.

8) Look at that bird, cried Dan, He's got my chips!

9) I'll never forget that day, sighed the elephant.

10) Duck! said Jack. No, it's a wasp! answered Ed.

11) Don't wander in the swamp, warned the dwarf.

12) Where's my hat? asked the mysterious woman.

13) You need eight fillings, said the dentist.

14) Oh no! cried Sam, Surely not that many!

15) I told you to brush your teeth, said the dentist.

16) I did, Sam wailed, I brushed them every day.

17) But you also ate ten Mars bars, the dentist said.

18) Can I play? little Jenny asked the older boys.

19) Go on then, they laughed, This should be funny!

20) Wow, the boys gasped, she's scored ten goals!

Extra sentences

E1) Stop that crying, said mum to dad, I'll buy you another ice lolly.

E2) I won't pretend I'm not worried, said Simon, because I am.

Speech marks

1) ....

2) ....

3) ....

4) ....

5) ....

6) ....

7) ....

8) ....

9) ....

10) ....

11) ....

12) ....

13) ....

14) ....

15) ....

16) ....

17) ....

18) ....

19) ....

20) ....

Extra sentences

E1) ....

E2) ....

Speech marks

1) Why are your feet so big? we asked the clown.

2) Stop shouting! shouted my dad.

3) I really love carrots, the carrot fan told me.

4) Say cheese! said the man with the camera.

5) But I don't like cheese, moaned Brian.

6) Oh no, said my uncle, I've lost my glasses!

7) My aunt said, They're on your head.

8) I can walk, swim and fly, the duck boasted.

9) Me too, said the pilot with armbands.

10) I feel as light as a feather, smiled the ballerina.

11) Not to me, gasped her partner, trying to lift her.

12) Think before you speak, the artist advised.

13) Can I have a scarf? the snowman asked.

14) Smelly cat, smelly cat, sang Phoebe.

15) Here kitty, said the lion-tamer nervously.

16) Hello, lunch, the lion replied with a grin.

17) Come on, you can do it! we cheered.

18) This is impossible, whispered the scientist.

19) I held out the dish and said, Have some more.

20) This is wonderful work, the teacher told us all.

Extra sentences

E1) What's in the box? we asked curiously, It's making a noise.

E2) Eek! screeched Sandra, There's a big spider on your head!

1) ....

2) ....

3) ....

4) ....

5) ....

6) ....

7) ....

8) ....

9) ....

10) ....

11) ....

12) ....

13) ....

14) ....

15) ....

16) ....

17) ....

18) ....

19) ....

20) ....

Extra sentences

E1) ....

E2) ....

Speech marks

Write out this passage, correcting the mistakes. A set of speech marks counts as one mistake. There are other mistakes too. You need [ ] correct to reach Punctuation Paradise.

Sam was quite surprised the day he found a wizard in his garden shed. Of course, he knew about witches and wizards from stories. But that's where they belonged — in stories. Not in sheds.

What are you doing in my dads shed? Sam asked. Look, you've knocked all his tools over.

Don't you take that tone with me, boy, said the wizard in a grumpy voice. I'm a wizard, I'll have you know.

I do know, said Sam, I can tell by the hat and the wand.

This seemed to cheer the wizard up. They're obviously teaching them something useful in these schools at last, he muttered to himself. Then he got to his feet and smiled at Sam.

Well then, boy I'm the Marvellous Magician Monty, at your service. Cousin of Merlin, you know.

I'm Sam, said Sam. Are you really at my service Do I get three wishes or something?

Certainly not, snapped monty, don't be so greedy. I'll turn one person into a pig for you, and that's your lot.

Great, smiled Sam, I know just the person. Do you know Nasty Norman in Year Five at my school?

Not yet, said Monty, with a wicked grin, but he'll know me soon enough!

Speech marks

Proof-reading

There was trouble on Greentoes Farm. the farmer couldn't understand what had got into the animals.

"We dont care what you say," said Noop the cow, "We want an end of term party"

"Well, you can't have one," the farmer told them. "Who do you think you are You're not at school, youre on a farm. You're not children you're animals."

He had a point, but the animals wouldn't listen.

it's not fair, said Cabbage the pig, "why should they have all the fun We work just as hard as school kids do, so we want an end of term party"

There was nothing the farmer could do Until he gave them a party the animals wouldnt do any more work. The sheep refused to grow their wool. Noop and the other cows wouldn't give him any milk The hens, Snowy and Bantam, kept feeding their eggs to cabbage the pig.

"For goodness sake," the farmer sighed, putting on a paper hat. "fine, you win. Let's have an end of term party."

The animals were delighted. There was music and dancing Cabbage the pig insisted they had jelly and ice cream. They played musical chairs, and noop the cow won after she sat on the farmer.

I can't wait for the summer holidays, she said happily

E4P21